G. Schirmer's Editions
of
Oratorios and Cantatas

—

THE MESSIAH

An Oratorio

For Four-Part Chorus of Mixed Voices,
Soprano, Alto, Tenor, and Bass Soli
and Piano

by

G. F. HANDEL

Edited by
T. TERTIUS NOBLE

Revised According to
Handel's Original Score by
MAX SPICKER

Vocal Score, Complete

Ed. 38

G. Schirmer, Inc.
New York

INTRODUCTORY NOTE

THE MESSIAH, Händel's most successful and best-known oratorio, was composed in the year 1741 in twenty-four days, from August the 22d to September the 14th. It was first performed at a concert given for charitable purposes at Dublin, Ireland, on April the 13th, 1742, Händel conducting the performance in person.

According to the historical evidence, Händel knew that the Dublin orchestral and choral resources were by no means on a par with those of London, and was markedly influenced by this circumstance in the composition of his work. In his choruses he did not go beyond four-part writing, and kept his orchestra within the most modest limits, so that no instrument except violin and trumpet plays a solo part, and oboe and bassoon do not appear at all in the score, although these instruments participated in the performance, as was proved by a later discovery of orchestra-parts written for both. Thereafter Händel, beginning with March the 23d, 1743, brought out *The Messiah* every year in London with great applause; in the course of time he made various alterations in certain numbers, set several new ones to music, transcribed a few arias for different voices, but left the work as a whole unchanged, both vocally and instrumentally, from its original form; thus bearing witness that, despite its limitations, this primitive conception of the work was likewise the enduring one.

As the centuries have passed, a considerable number of vocal scores have, of course, been made after Händel's partition; notably that by Dr. Clarke (Whitfield-Clarke, 1809), and a later one by Vincent Novello. Their value, however, was more or less doubtful, their character being rather that of transcriptions in pianoforte style, with not infrequent arbitrary or capricious aberrations, than a faithful and exact reduction of the orchestral score. Neither have the more recent editions of vocal scores based on the Mozart orchestra-score, with its many contrapuntal charms, quite fulfilled expectations, as they materially increased the difficulty of the piano-part.

Hence, a vocal score which should be in every way reliable and practical has become a matter of prime necessity. The present edition agrees at every point with Händel's original score, as it follows the facsimile edition of this latter with most careful exactitude. Slight deviations from the original, which in the course of many years have obtained almost traditional authority, are inserted in small notes in every case, the professional artist being left free to employ them or not, at his discretion.

With regard to the performance of this grand work by chorus and soloists, much of importance might be said; but this would lead too far afield, and we shall, therefore, confine ourselves to the matters of chiefest concern. The direction of the choruses, which in our Master's works are for the most part peculiarly prominent in their monumental character, will naturally be entrusted to competent chorus-conductors, who will care for crystalline precision of execution and a clear, logical conception, and who are responsible for these points.

The interpretation of their parts by the soloists is a different affair. Here we confront the weighty question: "May the soloist proceed subjectively, or must he proceed objectively?" Probably the best answer to this crucial query is found in a passage from the unrivalled work of an authority in this province, namely, "Die Lehre von der vokalen Ornamentik des 17. und 18. Jahrhunderts," by Dr. Hugo Goldschmidt. He writes: "The essence of reproduction, to feel and re-create that which was felt and imparted by the creator, does not exclude—within natural limitations—the assertion of creative power. The modern theory of æsthetics founded by Lipps rightly proceeds from the idea, that the interpreting artist creates, in a sense, the work anew. With his gradual penetration of the art-work he creates new values, which are of the highest importance for art, because, without them, the creations of the great masters are only so much writing, and thus remain sealed to enjoyment. But the interpreter's work is no mere execution, comparable, let us say, to that of the builder who transmutes the architect's plans into material reality. His task is rather to seize the vital conception of the art-work, to blend it with his own ego and the views of his period, and thus to imbue it with life and effectiveness. Whether singer or instrumentalist, he is a child of his time. His artistry is a product of its mental culture. It develops and changes with the evolution of artistic require ments. His formative and emotional powers are derived from the spirit of the epoch to which he belongs. Consequently, we shall always approach the art-productions of earlier times through the medium of our own spiritual and emotional nature. It follows, that the domain which such artistic reproduction may open to us, although of great extent, and as broad in scope as the points of contact with modern sensibility can reach, will be dependent in any given period on a constantly shifting relation to the treasures of former ages. The genuine, great masterworks of the past retain their importance; they are immortal; but our relations to them are not constant, and change with the changing impressionability of the times. We hear the works of these past-masters of former centuries—of Palestrina, Gabrieli, Händel and Bach, yes, even of Mozart and Beethoven—with other ears than our forefathers, or even than our grandfathers. What we have experienced since their time, whatever we have wrested to our eternal gain, this it is which sounds in those works to our ears. Much that charmed former generations has no effect on ours; so much is part and parcel of the time which gave it birth, and decays with its passing. Only what is exalted over time and place remains as eternal gain; and here, again, another generation finds new treasures that earlier ones passed by unheeding. This is the unfailing criterion of true greatness, that its creations continually beget ever-new, ever-changing values, that they bring to each successive generation new revelations. Consider the history of Händel's art. The eighteenth century, in its latter half, admired it in the form of arrangements by contemporaries, those by Mozart and Hiller. Our present-day musical interpretation—on Dr. Chrysander's initiative—has gone back to the historically authenticated form, and disclosed to us the true Händel in his full grandeur. But it owes its success, not to a recognition that things must be so because Händel would have them so, but because they appeal more directly to our sense and feeling than do the arrangements of the eighteenth and nineteenth centuries."

Such are the pregnant and weighty pronouncements of an experienced man, deeply versed in musico-historical lore and research. They should be of the highest value to the serious artist.

Here a word shall be said touching the employment of the appoggiaturas in the recitatives and (in isolated cases) also in the arias. They are, of course, not given in this edition, or indicated only very infrequently.

The Appoggiatura, in Händel's works, must be treated with the utmost caution and nicest discrimination. It should never be regarded as a mere ornament, but always fulfil some declamatory, melodic or harmonic function. Do not lose sight of the fact, that the appoggiatura lends greater elasticity and emphasis to the flow of melody and declamation, and also to the musical expression; at the same time, one cannot be too careful not to introduce it too often, for this would doubtless produce an unpleasing and inadmissible monotony instead of enhancing the effect.

According to historical evidence, Händel permitted his singers to employ appoggiaturas, and even melismata and cadences, in the arias of his oratorios; he invariably insisted, however, that they should not be mere embellishments serving simply for outward display of vocal effect, but calculated to promote the melodic flow and declamatory expression, and must, consequently, possess musical meaning and value. Mistakes in the use of these ornaments can be prevented only by a thorough knowledge of the development of vocal embellishments, a certain penetration into the spirit of Händel's oratorios, and a refined taste in matters pertaining to musical æsthetics.

The Appoggiatura is unquestionably the most important and most frequently employed among the ornaments, and a few general observations concerning the principles involved can hardly fail to be welcome; more especially as they are accompanied by a number of practical illustrations.

An appoggiatura is in place where its introduction brings about a diatonic succession, and more particularly across the bar, in order to avoid the leap of a third; for example in No. 5, page 26:

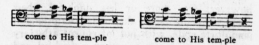

come to His tem-ple = come to His tem-ple

and similarly within the boundaries of one measure, as in No. 19, page 94:

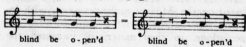

blind be o-pen'd = blind be o-pen'd

These latter must, however, be introduced with careful discrimination; otherwise appoggiaturas of this sort are very apt to produce a feeling of monotony and an interruption of the melodic flow. Another species of appoggiatura which may be used very effectively is the leap to the fourth below; this occurs both in the midst of a measure (No. 19, page 94):

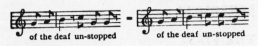

of the deaf un-stopped   of the deaf un-stopped

or (and far oftener) at the close of a recitative (No. 31, page 141):

was He stricken.   was He stricken.

Besides these, the leap of the appoggiatura to the sixth below is occasionally met with (No. 2, page 9):

is   par - don'd   is   par - don'd

The appoggiatura leading upward by a step is seldom or never employed; leading up by a leap it is very successfully applied in certain cases, for example in No. 2, page 9:

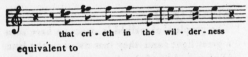

that cri - eth   in   the   wil - der - ness

equivalent to

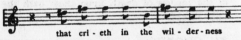

that cri - eth   in   the   wil - der - ness

or No. 8, page 47:

Em - man - u - el   Em - man - u - el

Great discretion and sound judgment are, however, very necessary for governing the employment of this upward-leaping appoggiatura; for if, in a quite analogous situation, as shown in No. 5, page 25:

the   dry   land,   all   na - tions,   I'll

the appoggiatura were introduced at the similar points:

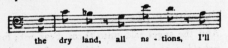

the   dry   land,   all   na - tions,   I'll

this would be, not simply a regrettable blunder, but a total misinterpretation of this important passage.

Illustrations of this kind show most convincingly how important it is that the singer should treat each case, as it arises, logically and discreetly, and how the appoggiatura, in apparently analogous situations, must sometimes be employed and at others avoided. The finest and most striking examples of this description, in our opinion, are those given by Händel in *The Messiah* on page 129 (No. 29): "Thy rebuke hath broken His heart," and on page 140 (No. 30): "Behold, and see." These two numbers, which are among the most beautiful, sublime and affecting of all that Händel has given us in his oratorios, and which convey a sense of mournful, hopeless anxiety in a manner of almost unparalleled realism, should be attentively studied by every oratorio-singer who truly loves his art.

We seize this occasion to direct attention to another important matter, which ought to be mentioned, if for no other reason, because it is unnoticed in all the other vocal scores. We refer to the chorus "Glory to God!" page 82 (No. 17). Here Händel inserted in his original score the following phrase: "da lontano e un poco piano" (as from a distance, and rather softly); and only thus should this chorus be performed. It appears to us that, relying on Händel's directions for the dynamics of this number, there can be no doubt that he intended a gradual approach (augmentation) of this solemn chant, as of an increasingly urgent, divinely inspired announcement, followed by an equally gradual *decrescendo* withdrawal. Supporting evidence is found in the postlude, which, after a grand *fortissimo* climax of the chorus, dies away to a whispered *pianissimo.—* The authenticity of the above reading has occasionally been called in question, with argument both in speech and writing; but such questioning can rest only on a lack of acquaintance—or an inexact acquaintance—with Händel's original score. So, in order to settle this important point definitively, we publish at the beginning of this edition a facsimile of the first page of this chorus from Händel's original manuscript, which should suffice to set the question at rest forever.

In our edition the greatest care has also been bestowed upon the word-text, and each number provided with a correct reference to the corresponding section in the Bible.

We can, therefore, publish this edition with the consciousness that it has been prepared with the throughness and reverent care due to this eternally beautiful masterwork.

MAX SPICKER.

New York, March, 1912.

THE MESSIAH

PART THE FIRST

I. OVERTURE

II. RECIT. *Accompanied.* (TENOR)
Comfort ye, comfort ye my people, saith your
God; speak ye comfortably to Jerusalem; and
cry unto her, that her warfare is accomplishèd,
that her iniquity is pardoned.

The voice of him that crieth in the wilderness, Prepare ye the way of the Lord, make
straight in the desert a highway for our God.

III. AIR (TENOR)
Every valley shall be exalted, and every mountain and hill made low; the crooked straight,
and the rough places plain.

IV. CHORUS
And the glory of the Lord shall be revealèd, and
all flesh shall see it together : for the mouth of
the Lord hath spoken it.

V. RECIT. *Accompanied.* (BASS)
Thus saith the Lord of Hosts :— Yet once a lit-
tle while and I will shake the heavens, and the
earth, the sea, and the dry land; and I will
shake all nations, and the desire of all nations
shall come.

The Lord, whom ye seek, shall suddenly come
to his temple, even the messenger of the cove-
nant, whom ye delight in; Behold, He shall
come, saith the Lord of Hosts.

VI. AIR (BASS)
But who may abide the day of His coming, and
who shall stand when He appeareth?

For He is like a refiner's fire.

VII. CHORUS
And He shall purify the sons of Levi, that they
may offer unto the Lord an offering in righteous-
ness

VIII. RECIT. (ALTO)
Behold, a virgin shall conceive, and bear a Son,
and shall call his name EMMANUEL, God with
us.

IX. AIR (ALTO) **AND CHORUS**
O thou that tellest good tidings to Zion, get
thee up into the high mountain; O thou that
tellest good tidings to Jerusalem, lift up thy
voice with strength; lift it up, be not afraid;
say unto the cities of Judah, Behold your God!

Arise, shine, for thy light is come, and the
glory of the Lord is risen upon thee.

X. RECIT. *Accompanied.* (BASS)
For, behold, darkness shall cover the earth, and
gross darkness the people; but the Lord shall
arise upon thee, and His glory shall be seen
upon thee, and the Gentiles shall come to thy
light, and kings to the brightness of thy rising.

XI. AIR (BASS)
The people that walkèd in darkness have seen
a great light : and they that dwell in the land
of the shadow of death, upon them hath the
light shinèd.

XII. CHORUS
For unto us a Child is born, unto us a Son is
given, and the government shall be upon His
shoulder : and His name shall be called Won-
derful, Counsellor, the Mighty God, the Everlasting Father, the Prince of Peace.

XIII. PASTORAL SYMPHONY

XIV. RECIT. (SOPRANO)
There were shepherds abiding in the field,
keeping watch over their flocks by night.

RECIT. *Accompanied.* (SOPRANO)
And lo! the angel of the Lord came upon them,
and the glory of the Lord shone round about
them, and they were sore afraid.

XV. RECIT. (SOPRANO)
And the angel said unto them, Fear not; for,
behold, I bring you good tidings of great joy,
which shall be to all people.

For unto you is born this day in the city of
David a Saviour, which is Christ the Lord.

XVI. RECIT. *Accompanied.* (SOPRANO)

And suddenly there was with the angel a multitude of the heavenly host praising God, and saying:

XVII. CHORUS

Glory to God in the highest, and peace on earth, good will towards men.

XVIII. AIR (SOPRANO)

Rejoice greatly, O daughter of Zion; Shout, O daughter of Jerusalem: behold, thy king cometh unto thee.

He is the righteous Saviour, and He shall speak peace unto the heathen.

XIX. RECIT. (ALTO)

Then shall the eyes of the blind be opened, and the ears of the deaf unstoppèd; then shall the lame man leap as an hart, and the tongue of the dumb shall sing.

XX. AIR (ALTO)

He shall feed His flock like a shepherd; and He shall gather the lambs with His arm, and carry them in His bosom, and gently lead those that are with young.

AIR (SOPRANO)

Come unto Him, all ye that labour and are heavy laden, and He shall give you rest.

Take His yoke upon you, and learn of Him; for He is meek and lowly of heart: and ye shall find rest unto your souls.

XXI. CHORUS

His yoke is easy and His burthen is light.

PART THE SECOND

XXII. CHORUS

Behold the Lamb of God, that taketh away the sins of the world.

XXIII. AIR (ALTO)

He was despisèd and rejected of men: a man of sorrows, and acquainted with grief.

*[He gave His back to the smiters, and His cheeks to them that plucked off the hair: He hid not His face from shame and spitting.]

XXIV. CHORUS

Surely He hath borne our griefs, and carried our sorrows; He was wounded for our transgressions; He was bruised for our iniquities; the chastisement of our peace was upon Him.

XXV. CHORUS

And with His stripes we are healèd.

XXVI. CHORUS

All we like sheep have gone astray; we have turnèd every one to his own way; and the Lord hath laid on Him the iniquity of us all.

XXVII. RECIT. *Accompanied.* (TENOR)

All they that see Him, laugh Him to scorn, they shoot out their lips, and shake their heads, saying:—

XXVIII. CHORUS

He trusted in God that He would deliver Him; let Him deliver Him, if He delight in Him.

XXIX. RECIT. *Accompanied.* (TENOR)

Thy rebuke hath broken His heart; He is full of heaviness. He looked for some to have pity on Him, but there was no man; neither found He any to comfort Him.

XXX. AIR (TENOR)

Behold, and see if there be any sorrow like unto His sorrow.

XXXI. RECIT. *Accompanied.* (TENOR)

He was cut off out of the land of the living: for the transgression of Thy people was He stricken.

XXXII. AIR (TENOR)

But Thou didst not leave His soul in hell; nor didst Thou suffer Thy Holy One to see corruption.

XXXIII. CHORUS

Lift up your heads, O ye gates; and be ye lift up, ye everlasting doors; and the King of glory shall come in.

Who is the King of glory? The Lord strong

*See Note, p. ix.

[vii]

and mighty, the Lord mighty in battle.

Lift up your heads, O ye gates; and be ye lift up, ye everlasting doors; and the King of glory shall come in.

Who is the King of glory? The Lord of Hosts, He is the King of glory.

XXXIV. RECIT. (Tenor)

Unto which of the angels said He at any time, Thou art my Son, this day have I begotten Thee?

XXXV. CHORUS

Let all the angels of God worship Him.

XXXVI. AIR* (Bass)

[Thou art gone up on high, Thou hast led captivity captive, and receivèd gifts for men; yea, even for Thine enemies, that the Lord God might dwell among them.]

XXXVII. CHORUS

The Lord gave the word: great was the company of the preachers.

XXXVIII. AIR (Soprano)

How beautiful are the feet of them that preach the gospel of peace, and bring glad tidings of good things.

XXXIX. CHORUS

Their sound is gone out into all lands, and their words unto the ends of the world.

XL. AIR (Bass)

Why do the nations so furiously rage together? [and] why do the people imagine a vain thing?

The kings of the earth rise up, and the rulers take counsel together against the Lord, and against His Anointed.

XLI. CHORUS

Let us break their bonds asunder, and cast away their yokes from us.

XLII. RECIT. (Tenor)

He that dwelleth in heaven shall laugh them to scorn; the Lord shall have them in derision.

XLIII. AIR (Tenor)

Thou shalt break them with a rod of iron; Thou shalt dash them in pieces like a potter's vessel.

XLIV. CHORUS

Hallelujah! for the Lord God omnipotent reigneth.

The kingdom of this world is become the kingdom of our Lord, and of His Christ; and He shall reign for ever and ever.

King of Kings, and Lord of Lords. Hallelujah!

PART THE THIRD

XLV. AIR (Soprano)

I know that my Redeemer liveth, and that He shall stand at the latter day upon the earth:

And though worms destroy this body, yet in my flesh shall I see God.

For now is Christ risen from the dead, the first-fruits of them that sleep.

XLVI. CHORUS

Since by man came death, by man came also the resurrection of the dead. For as in Adam all die, even so in Christ shall all be made alive.

XLVII. RECIT. Accompanied. (Bass)

Behold, I tell you a mystery: We shall not all sleep; but we shall all be changed in a moment, in the twinkling of an eye, at the last trumpet.

XLVIII. AIR (Bass)

The trumpet shall sound, and the dead shall be raised incorruptible, and we shall be changed.

*[For this corruptible must put on incorruption, and this mortal must put on immortality.]

* See Note, p. ix.

XLIX. RECIT. (Alto) *See Note, below.*
[*Then* shall be brought to pass the saying that is written: Death is swallowed up in victory.

L. DUET (Alto and Tenor)
O death, where is thy sting? O grave, where is thy victory? The sting of death is sin, and the strength of sin is the law.

LI. CHORUS
But thanks be to God, who giveth us the victory through our Lord Jesus Christ.

LII. AIR (Soprano)
If God be for us, who can be against us? who shall lay any thing to the charge of God's elect?

It is God that justifieth, who is he that condemneth?

It is Christ that died, yea, rather, that is risen again, who is at the right hand of God, who makes intercession for us.]

LIII. CHORUS
Worthy is the Lamb that was slain, and hath redeemed us to God by His blood, to receive power, and riches, and wisdom, and strength, and honour, and glory, and blessing.

Blessing and honour, glory and power, be unto Him that sitteth upon the throne, and unto the Lamb, for ever and ever.

Amen.

NOTE

The latter part of Nos. 23 and 48 and the whole of Nos. 34, 35, 36, 49, 50, 51, and 52 are customarily omitted.

Nos 1-21 and 44 are regarded as especially suitable for performance at Christmas.

INDEX
PART THE FIRST

NO.			PAGE
1. Overture			3
2. Recit. accompanied (*Tenor*)		*Comfort ye my people*	7
3. Air (*Tenor*)		*Every valley shall be exalted*	10
4. Chorus		*And the glory of the Lord*	16
5. Recit. accompanied (*Bass*)		*Thus saith the Lord*	24
6. Air (*Bass*)		*But who may abide the day of His coming?*	27
7. Chorus		*And He shall purify*	36
8. Recitative (*Alto*)		*Behold, a virgin shall conceive*	47
9. Air (*Alto*) and Chorus		*O thou that tellest good tidings to Zion*	47
10. Recit. accompanied (*Bass*)		*For, behold, darkness shall cover the earth*	60
11. Air (*Bass*)		*The people that walkèd in darkness*	62
12. Chorus		*For unto us a Child is born*	66
13. Pastoral Symphony			77
14. Recitative (*Soprano*)		*There were shepherds abiding in the field*	79
	Recit accompanied (*Soprano*)	*And lo! the angel of the Lord came upon them*	79
15. Recitative (*Soprano*)		*And the angel said unto them*	80
16. Recit. accompanied (*Soprano*)		*And suddenly there was with the angel*	81
17. Chorus		*Glory to God*	82
18. Air (*Soprano*)		*Rejoice greatly, O daughter of Zion*	87
19. Recitative (*Alto*)		*Then shall the eyes of the blind be opened*	94
20. Air (*Alto*)		*He shall feed His flock like a shepherd*	94
21. Chorus		*His yoke is easy, and His burthen is light*	98

PART THE SECOND

22. Chorus		*Behold the Lamb of God*	104
23. Air (*Alto*)		*He was despisèd*	108
24. Chorus		*Surely He hath borne our griefs*	113
25. Chorus		*And with His stripes we are healèd*	117
26. Chorus		*All we like sheep have gone astray*	122
27. Recit. accompanied (*Tenor*)		*All they that see Him, laugh Him to scorn*	131
28 Chorus		*He trusted in God that He would deliver Him*	132
29. Recit. accompanied (*Tenor*)		*Thy rebuke hath broken His heart*	139
30. Air (*Tenor*)		*Behold, and see if there be any sorrow*	140
31. Recit. accompanied (*Tenor*)		*He was cut off out of the land of the living*	141
32. Air (*Tenor*)		*But Thou didst not leave His soul in hell*	141
33. Chorus		*Lift up your heads, O ye gates*	144
34. Recitative (*Tenor*)		*Unto which of the angels said He*	153
35. Chorus		*Let all the angels of God worship Him*	153
36. Air (*Bass*)		*Thou art gone up on high*	158
37. Chorus		*The Lord gave the word*	163
38. Air (*Soprano*)		*How beautiful are the feet of them*	167
39. Chorus		*Their sound is gone out into all lands*	169

NO.			PAGE
40.	Air (*Bass*)	*Why do the nations so furiously rage*	174
41.	Chorus	*Let us break their bonds asunder*	182
42.	Recitative (*Tenor*)	*He that dwelleth in heaven*	189
43.	Air (*Tenor*)	*Thou shalt break them*	189
44.	Chorus	*Hallelujah!*	193

PART THE THIRD

45.	Air (*Soprano*)	*I know that my Redeemer liveth*	204
46.	Chorus	*Since by man came death*	210
47.	Recit. accompanied (*Bass*)	*Behold, I tell you a mystery*	214
48.	Air (*Bass*)	*The trumpet shall sound*	214
49.	Recitative (*Alto*)	*Then shall be brought to pass*	222
50.	Duet (*Alto and Tenor*)	*O death, where is thy sting?*	222
51.	Chorus	*But thanks be to God*	225
52.	Air (*Soprano*)	*If God be for us, who can be against us?*	231
53.	Chorus	*Worthy is the Lamb*	237

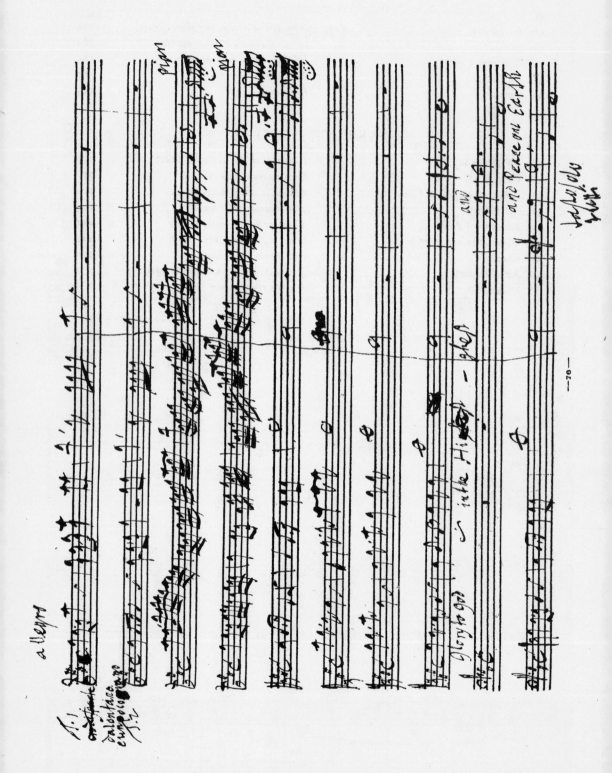

THE MESSIAH

PART I

Nº 1. – OVERTURE

G. F. Händel

Nº 2. – RECITATIVE FOR TENOR

"COMFORT YE MY PEOPLE"

Isaiah xl: 1-3

saith your God, saith your God;

speak ye com-fort-a-bly to Je - ru - sa-lem, speak ye

com-fort-a -bly to Je - ru - sa-lem, and cry un-to her that her

war - fare, her war - fare is ac-complished, that her in -

Original orchestral score has:

1) cry un-to her

2) is ac- com-plish'd

i - qui-ty is par-don'd, that her in - i - qui-ty is par - -

don'd.

mf

C

The voice of him that crieth in the wilderness, Pre-pare ye the way of the

Lord, make straight in the desert a high-way for our God.

Nº 3.– AIR FOR TENOR
"Every valley shall be exalted"

Isaiah xl: 4

Andante (♩ = 80)

the crook-ed straight, and the rough plac-es

plain, _____ the crook-ed

straight, the crook - ed straight, and rough plac-es plain, _____

cresc.

p

simile

and the rough plac-es plain.

p   *mf*

C

Ev-'ry val-ley,   ev-'ry val-ley

p   *f*   *p*

shall be ex-alt - - - - - -

- - - - - -ed,

f

and the rough plac-es plain, and the rough plac-es

plain, _____ the crook-ed straight,

ad lib. E

and the rough plac - es plain.

colla voce *a tempo*

senza Ped.

Nº 4. – CHORUS

"AND THE GLORY OF THE LORD"

Isaiah xl: 5

*) According to the original score.

№5. – RECITATIVE FOR BASS

"THUS SAITH THE LORD"

all na-tions; I'll

shake the heav'ns, the earth, the sea, the

dry land, all na-tions, I'll shake, and the de -

sire

cresc.

*)Other editions have *C* here; according to the original score, however, *E* is correct.
22945

of all na - tions shall come.

B *Recit.*

The Lord whom ye seek shall suddenly come to His tem-ple, ev'n the

mes-sen-ger of the cov - e -nant, whom ye de - light in;

Be-hold, he shall come, saith the Lord of Hosts.

Nº 6. – AIR FOR BASS

"BUT WHO MAY ABIDE THE DAY OF HIS COMING?"

Malachi iii: 2

Larghetto (♪ = 88)

BASS SOLO A

But who may a-

bide the day of His com-ing? and who shall stand when

He __ ap-pear-eth? who shall __ stand when

for He is like ____ a re-

fin - - - - - - - -

- - - - er's_ fire.____

E

Who shall stand when He ap-

pear - eth? For He is like a re-

F Larghetto (Tempo I)

But who may a - bide the day of His coming?

and who shall stand, and who shall stand when He ap -

peareth? when He ap - peareth?

G Prestissimo

For He is like ___ a re - fin - - er's

fire, ___ like a re - fin - - er's ___

I Adagio

er's fire, for He is like a re - fin - er's

Prestissimo

fire.

STAUD

Nº 7.– CHORUS
"AND HE SHALL PURIFY"

Malachi iii: 3

Nº 8.– RECITATIVE FOR ALTO
"BEHOLD! A VIRGIN SHALL CONCEIVE"

Nº 9.– AIR FOR ALTO, AND CHORUS
"O THOU THAT TELLEST GOOD TIDINGS TO ZION"

up in-to the high moun - - - - - - - - - -

- - - tain! get thee up in-to the high

moun - - - - - - - - - -

C

- - tain!

CHORUS

Lord _____ is ris - en up - on thee

Lord _____ is ris - en up - on thee.

Lord _____ is ris - en up - on thee.

Lord _____ is ris - en up - on thee.

allargando

Nº 10.– RECITATIVE FOR BASS
"FOR BEHOLD, DARKNESS SHALL COVER THE EARTH"

Isaiah lx: 2,3

A

but the Lord shall a - rise

poco cresc.

up - on thee, and His

glo - - - ry shall be seen up - on thee, and His

glo - - ry shall be seen up - on thee. And the Gentiles shall

come to thy light, and kings to the brightness of thy ris - ing.

Nº 11.– AIR FOR BASS
"THE PEOPLE THAT WALKED IN DARKNESS"

Isaiah ix: 2

on__ them hath the light shin - - ed, and

they that dwell,__ that dwell in the land of the shad - - - -

- - ow of death, up - on__ them hath the

light _____ shin - ed, up - on__ them hath the light shin - ed.

Nº 12. – CHORUS
"FOR UNTO US A CHILD IS BORN"

Isaiah ix: 6

Andante allegro (♩ = 76)

76

22945

Nº 13.
PASTORAL SYMPHONY

STANN

Nº 14. – RECITATIVE FOR SOPRANO
"There were shepherds abiding in the field"

Luke ii: 8

RECITATIVE FOR SOPRANO
"And lo! the angel of the Lord came upon them"

Luke ii: 9

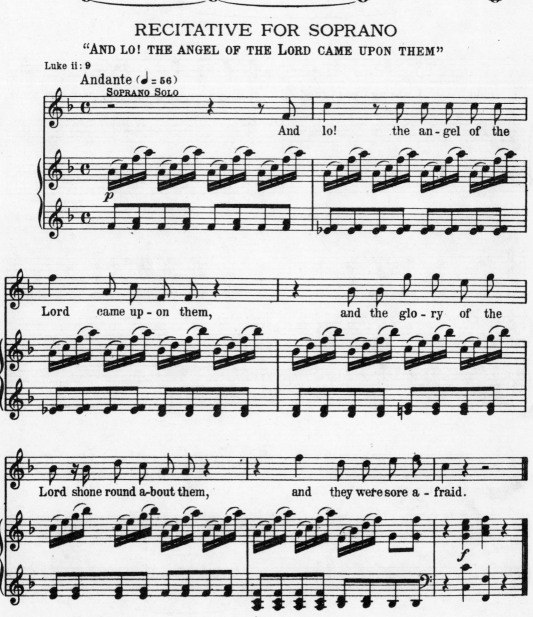

№ 15. – RECITATIVE FOR SOPRANO
"AND THE ANGEL SAID UNTO THEM"

Luke ii: **10,11**

SOPRANO SOLO

And the an-gel said un-to them, Fear not: for be-hold, I bring you good ti-dings of great joy, which shall be to all peo-ple. For un-to you is born this day in the cit-y of Da-vid a Sav-iour, which is Christ the Lord.

Nº 16. – RECITATIVE FOR SOPRANO

"AND SUDDENLY THERE WAS WITH THE ANGEL"

Luke ii: 13

Nᵒ 17. – CHORUS
"GLORY TO GOD"

Luke ii: 14

№ 18. – AIR FOR SOPRANO
"REJOICE GREATLY, O DAUGHTER OF ZION!"

Zechariah ix: 9, 10

O daughter of Zi-on! re-joice,_____ re-joice,_____

re-joice!

B

O daugh-ter of Zi-on! Re - joice_____ great-ly,

shout,_____ O daugh-ter of Je-ru-sa-lem: be-

hold, thy king com-eth un - to thee, be -

hold, thy king cometh un - to — thee, cometh un-to thee;

C Meno mosso

He is_ the

right - - eous Sav-iour, and he shall speak

Be-hold, thy_ king com-eth un - to thee, re-joice,_____

re-joice_____

and shout, shout, shout, shout, re-joice_

greatly,

re - joice___ great-ly, O daugh-ter of Zi - on! shout,___

O daugh-ter of Je- - ru - sa-lem! Be-hold, thy

king com-eth un - - to thee, be-hold, thy king com-eth un - to

thee.

Nº 19. – RECITATIVE FOR ALTO
"THEN SHALL THE EYES OF THE BLIND BE OPENED"

Isaiah xxxv: 5,6

*)In the original score, this is given to the Soprano, in the key of G. But, as the first part of Nº **20** is usually sung by a Contralto, it is better that the Recitative should be sung by the same voice.

Nº 20. – AIR FOR ALTO
"HE SHALL FEED HIS FLOCK LIKE A SHEPHERD"

Isaiah xl: **11** – Matt. xi: **28, 29**

*)Often sung thus:

He_ is_ meek_ and low - ly of heart, and ye_ shall find rest,_ and ye shall find rest un - to_ your souls.

Take His yoke up-on you, and learn of Him, for He_ is_ meek_ and low - ly of heart, and ye shall find rest, and ye shall find rest un - to_ your souls.

STAND

Nº 21. – CHORUS
"HIS YOKE IS EASY, AND HIS BURTHEN IS LIGHT"

Matthew xi : 30

*) Original score has in bass here:

END OF PART I

PART II

Nº 22. – CHORUS

"BEHOLD THE LAMB OF GOD"

C

the sins of the world,

tak-eth a-way the sins, the sins of the world, the sins of the

_mf_
that tak-eth a-way the sins of the world, the sins of the

_mf_
that tak-eth a-way the sins of the world, the sins of the

C

the sins of the world, that tak-eth a-way the sins of the

world, the sins of the world, that tak-eth a-way the sins of the

world, the sins of the world, that tak-eth a-way the sins of the

world, that tak-eth a-way the sins of the

*)

world.

world.

world.

world.

*) Original score:

22045

N⁰ 23. – AIR FOR ALTO
"HE WAS DESPISED"

Isaiah liii: 3; 1:6

ALTO SOLO **A**

He was des-pis-ed,

des-pis-ed and re-ject-ed,   re-

ject-ed of men;   a man of sor - - -rows,

*) Original score:

a man of sor - - rows, and ac- quainted with grief, ___

___ a man of sor-rows, and ac- quainted with grief.

He

was des-pis-ed, re-ject-ed, He was des-

*) Original score has *a♭* here, but usually *a♮* is sung instead.

№945

pis-ed and re-ject-ed of men; a man of sorrows, and acquainted with

grief, _____ a man of sor-rows, and ac-quaint-ed with grief.

He was despis-ed, re-ject-ed; a man of

sorrows, and acquainted with grief, and acquainted with grief, _____

a man of sorrows, and ac-quaint-ed with grief.

Fine **E**

He gave His back to the

Fine *Un poco piano*

smit-ers, He gave His back to the

smit-ers, and His cheeks to them that plucked off the

hair, and His cheeks to them that plucked off the

Nº 24. – CHORUS
"SURELY HE HATH BORNE OUR GRIEFS"

Isaiah liii: 4, 5

Nº 25. – CHORUS

"AND WITH HIS STRIPES WE ARE HEALED"

Nº 26. – CHORUS

"ALL WE LIKE SHEEP HAVE GONE ASTRAY"

Isaiah liii: 6

№. 27. – RECITATIVE FOR TENOR

"ALL THEY THAT SEE HIM, LAUGH HIM TO SCORN"

Psalm xxii: 7

Nº 28. – CHORUS

"He trusted in God that He would deliver Him"

Psalm xxii: 8

Allegro

Nᵒ 29. – RECITATIVE FOR TENOR

"THY REBUKE HATH BROKEN HIS HEART"

Psalm lxix: 20

Largo

№ 30. – AIR FOR TENOR

"Behold, and see if there be any sorrow"

Lamentations i: 12

№. 31. – RECITATIVE FOR TENOR

"HE WAS CUT OFF OUT OF THE LAND OF THE LIVING"

Isaiah liii: 8

№. 32. – AIR FOR TENOR

"BUT THOU DIDST NOT LEAVE HIS SOUL IN HELL"

Psalm xvi: 10

Andante larghetto (♪ = 108)

*) This is according to Händel's score; other editions have not the appoggiatura:

Nº 33. – CHORUS

"LIFT UP YOUR HEADS, O YE GATES"

Psalm xxiv: 7-10

G. F. Händel

*) Händel's score has here, and in all similar cases, "this" King, not "the" King. It has become traditional, however, to sing "the" King.

strong and

*) № 34. – RECITATIVE FOR TENOR

"Unto which of the angels said He"

Hebrews 1: 5

*) № 35. – CHORUS

"Let all the angels of God worship Him"

Hebrews 1: 6

*)Nº 36. – AIR FOR BASS

"Thou art gone up on high"

Psalm lxviii: 18

Allegro (♩ = 84)

Thou art gone up on high, Thou art gone up on high,

Thou hast led cap-tiv - i - ty cap-tive, Thou hast led cap-tiv- i - ty

cap-tive, and re - ceiv - - - ed gifts___ for men; yea,

*)Generally omitted.

might dwell a-mong them.

Thou art gone up on high, Thou art gone up on high, Thou hast

led cap-tiv - i - ty cap-tive, Thou hast led cap-tiv - i - ty cap-tive,

and re - ceiv - ed gifts for men; yea, e - ven

for Thine en - - - - - - - - - -

God might dwell a-   - mong them, might dwell_____

a-mong

them,   that the Lord God might dwell a-mong them.

Nº 37. – CHORUS

"THE LORD GAVE THE WORD"

Psalm lxviii: 11

-pa-ny of the preach-ers,

-pa-ny, the com-pa-ny of the preach-ers,

com- -pa-ny of the preach-ers,

-pa-ny of the preach-ers,

great was the com-pa-ny of the preachers. The Lord gave the word;

great was the com-pa-ny of the preachers. The Lord gave the word;

great was the com-pa-ny of the preachers.

great was the com-pa-ny of the preachers.

great was the com- -pa-ny, the com-

great was the com- -pa-ny, the com-

Great was the com-pa-ny, the com- -pa-ny, the

Great was the com- pa-ny, the com- -pa-ny, the

Nº 38.– AIR FOR SOPRANO

"HOW BEAUTIFUL ARE THE FEET OF THEM"

Romans x: 15

Larghetto (♪ = 104)

SOPRANO SOLO

How beau-ti-ful are the feet of them that preach the gos-pel of peace, how beau-ti-ful are the feet, how beau-ti-ful are the feet of them that preach the gos-pel of peace, how beau-ti-ful are the feet of them that

Nº 39. – CHORUS

"THEIR SOUND IS GONE OUT INTO ALL LANDS"

22945

№ 40 – AIR FOR BASS

"WHY DO THE NATIONS SO FURIOUSLY RAGE TOGETHER?"

Psalm ii: **1,2**

Allegro (♩ = 112)

A BASS SOLO

Why do the na- - -tions so fu-rious-ly rage to-geth - er? why do the peo- -ple im-a - gine a vain thing? Why do the na- -tions

rage

so fu-rious-ly to-geth-er? why do the peo-ple im-a- - - - - - - - -gine a vain

thing?_____ im - a - - - - - -

B

- -gine a vain thing?

Why do the na - tions so fu - riously rage to-

geth- -er, and why do the

peo-ple, and why do the

peo-ple im- -a- -gine a_ vain_ thing?_ Why do the na- -tions rage _ so furiously to - gether, so furiously to - geth - er? and

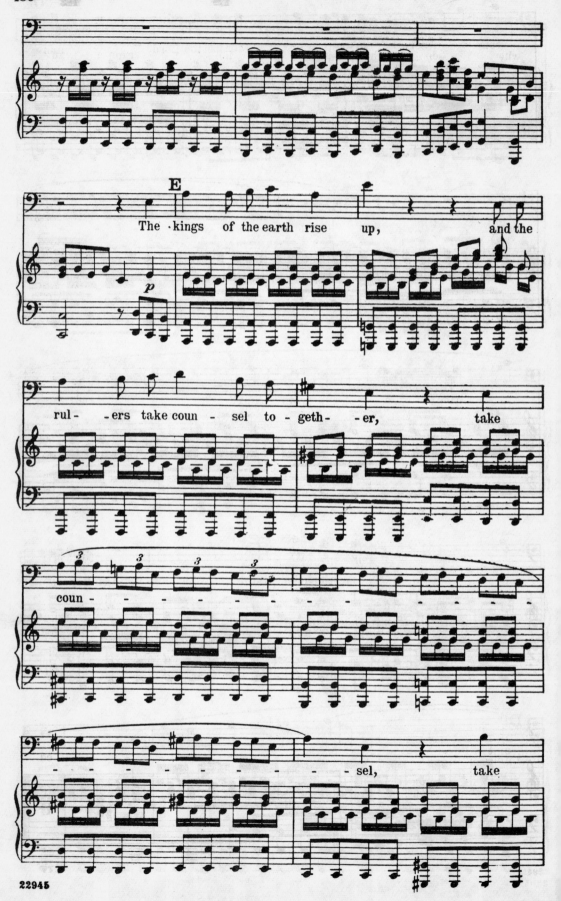

Nº 41. – CHORUS

"LET US BREAK THEIR BONDS ASUNDER"

Psalm ii: 3

let us break their bonds, and cast_____ a- -way, and cast a-

bonds, their bonds a- -sun- -der, and cast a- -way, and cast a-

sun- -der, their bonds a- -sun- -der, and cast a- -way, and cast a-

let us break their bonds a- -sun- -der, and cast a- -way, and cast a-

way their yokes from us.

way their yokes from us.

way their yokes___ from us.

way their yokes from us.

Nº42.–RECITATIVE FOR TENOR
"HE THAT DWELLETH IN HEAVEN"

He that dwell-eth in hea-ven shall laugh them to scorn; the Lord shall have them in de-ri-sion.

Nº43.–AIR FOR TENOR
"THOU SHALT BREAK THEM"

Thou shalt break them, Thou shalt break them with a rod of i-ron;

Thou shalt dash them in piec-es like a pot——ter's

ves-sel, Thou shalt dash them in piec-es, in

cresc.

piec-es like a pot————

B

——ter's ves-sel.

f

Thou shalt break them,

STAND

№ 44.– CHORUS

"HALLELUJAH!"

Rev. xix: 6; xi: 15; xix: 16

Allegro (♩=72)

Organ or Piano

*) Händel's score has one 8th note e here only; see foot-note on next page.

196

*) Händel's score has here ♩♪♪ 2 syllables for one note, it is therefore better to substitute two 16th notes for the 8th

22945

END OF PART II

PART III

№ 45.– AIR FOR SOPRANO

"I KNOW THAT MY REDEEMER LIVETH"

Job xix: 25, 26; 1 Cor. xv: 20

205

stand _____ at the lat - - - ter day up - on the earth,

up - on __ the earth:

cresc.

D

And though worms de - stroy this bod - y,

yet in my flesh shall I see

208

22945

Nº 46.– CHORUS

"SINCE BY MAN CAME DEATH"

1 Cor. xv: 21

Nᵒ 47. – RECITATIVE FOR BASS

"BEHOLD, I TELL YOU A MYSTERY"

1 Cor. xv: **51, 52**

Nᵒ 48. – AIR FOR BASS

"THE TRUMPET SHALL SOUND"

1 Cor. xv: **52, 53**

BASS SOLO %A

The trum-pet shall sound, _____ and the dead shall be

raised, and the dead shall be raised _____ in-cor-

rup-ti-ble; the

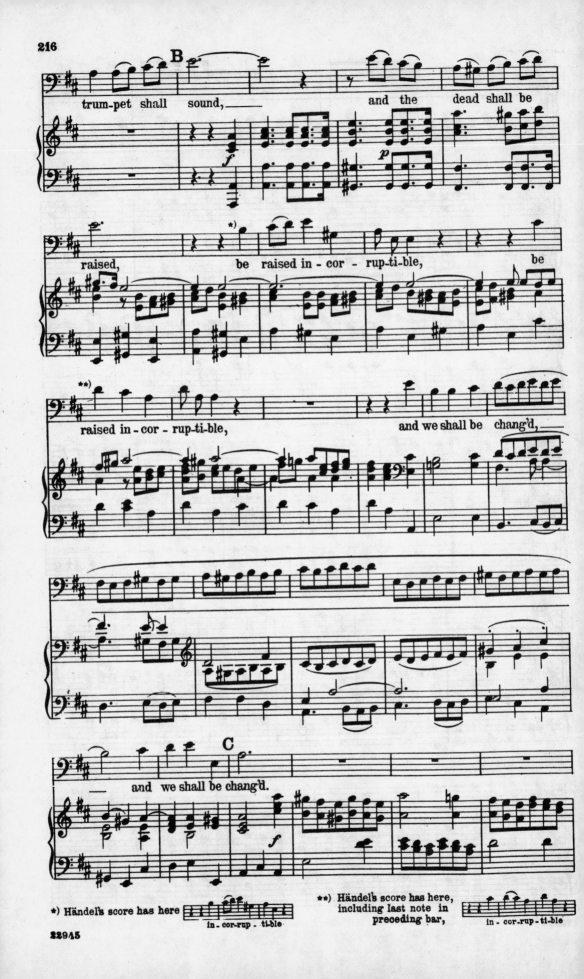

trum-pet shall sound, _____ and the dead shall be

raised, be raised in - cor - rup-ti-ble, be

raised in - cor - rup-ti-ble, and we shall be chang'd, _____

and we shall be chang'd.

*) Händel's score has here **in - cor-rup - ti-ble**

) Händel's score has here, including last note in preceding bar, **in - cor-rup-ti-ble

The trum-pet shall sound,____ the trum-pet shall sound,____ and the dead shall be raised,____ be raised in - cor - rup-ti-ble, be raised in - cor - rup-ti-ble, and

we shall be chang'd, be chang'd,_____

and we shall be chang'd,

and we shall be chang'd,_____ we

shall be chang'd,_____ we shall be

chang'd, and we shall be chang'd,_____

and we shall be chang'd, we shall be chang'd,_____ and we shall be chang'd, we shall be chang'd.

Adagio **G** *a tempo*

f a tempo

p

Fine

220

For this cor - rup - ti - ble must put on in - - cor - rup - tion,

for this cor - rup - ti - ble must put on,

must put on, _____

_____ must put on, must put on in - - cor - rup - tion;

cresc.

and this mor - tal must put _____ on im-mor-

*) This section is generally omitted.

22945

tal - - - - - - - - i-ty, and this mor - tal must put on im-mor - tal - - - - - mor - - - i-ty, im-mor - tal - i - ty. The

STAND TO/END

*) № 49.– RECITATIVE FOR ALTO
"THEN SHALL BE BROUGHT TO PASS"

1 Cor. xv: 54

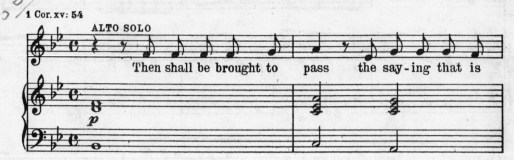

ALTO SOLO

Then shall be brought to pass the say-ing that is writ-ten, Death is swal-low'd up in vic-to-ry.

*) Nos. 49, 50, 51, 52 are generally omitted.

№ 50.– DUET FOR ALTO AND TENOR
"O DEATH, WHERE IS THY STING?"

1 Cor. xv: 55, 56

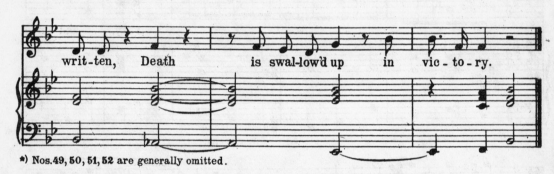

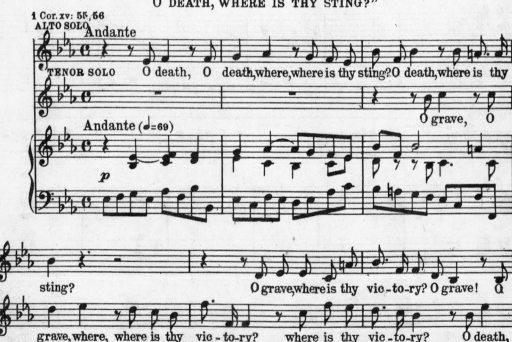

ALTO SOLO Andante

TENOR SOLO O death, O death, where, where is thy sting? O death, where is thy

O grave, O

Andante (♩=69)

sting? O grave, where is thy vic-to-ry? O grave! O

grave, where, where is thy vic-to-ry? where is thy vic-to-ry? O death,

N.B.– This Duet is given in the abridged form indicated by Händel in the Dublin score. Compare the **Full Score**.

death, O death, where, where is thy sting? where, O grave, where is thy

where, where is thy sting? where, where is thy sting? O grave, where is thy

A

vic - to - ry? O death, where, where is thy sting? O grave,—

vic - to - ry? O grave! O death, where, where is thy sting? O

A

— O grave, where is thy vic - to - ry? O grave,—where is thy

grave, O grave, where is thy vic - to - ry? O grave.— where is thy

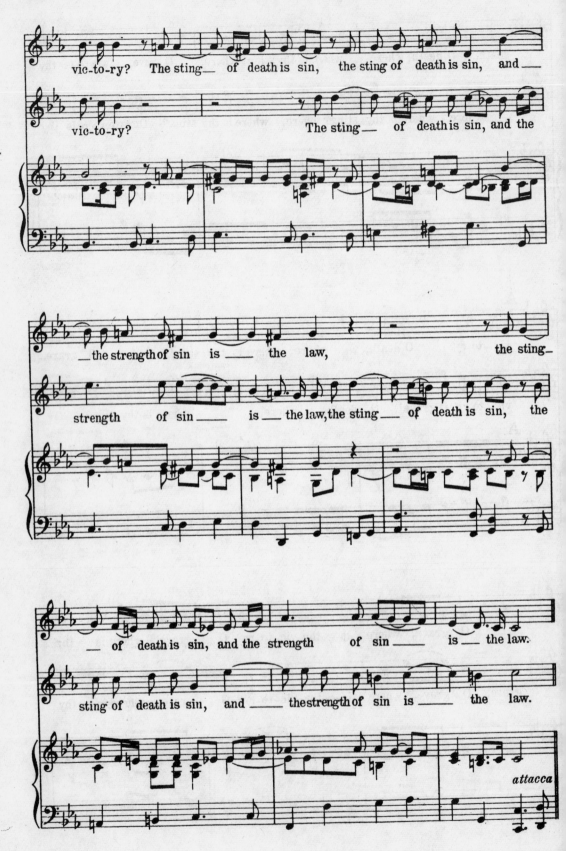

Nº 51. – CHORUS
"But thanks be to God"

1 Cor. xv: 57

226

22945

22945

Nº 52.– AIR FOR SOPRANO
"IF GOD BE FOR US, WHO CAN BE AGAINST US?"

Romans viii: **31,33,34**

*) Händel's score has here:

22945

If God be for us, who

gainst us? If God be for us, who can be a-

gainst us?

B

Who shall lay an-y-thing to the charge of God's e - lect?

of God's e - lect?

Who shall lay an-y-thing to the charge

ces - - - - sion for us, who is at the

right hand of God, who is at the right hand of God, at the right hand of

Adagio

God, who makes in-ter - ces-sion for us.

ad lib. *f a tempo*

Nº 53. – CHORUS

"Worthy is the Lamb that was slain"

Rev. v: 12,13

Largo

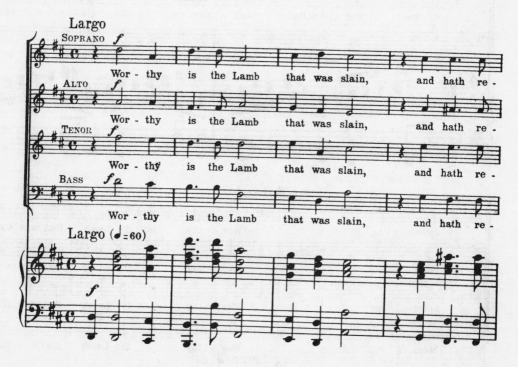

*) See foot-note on page 196.

246

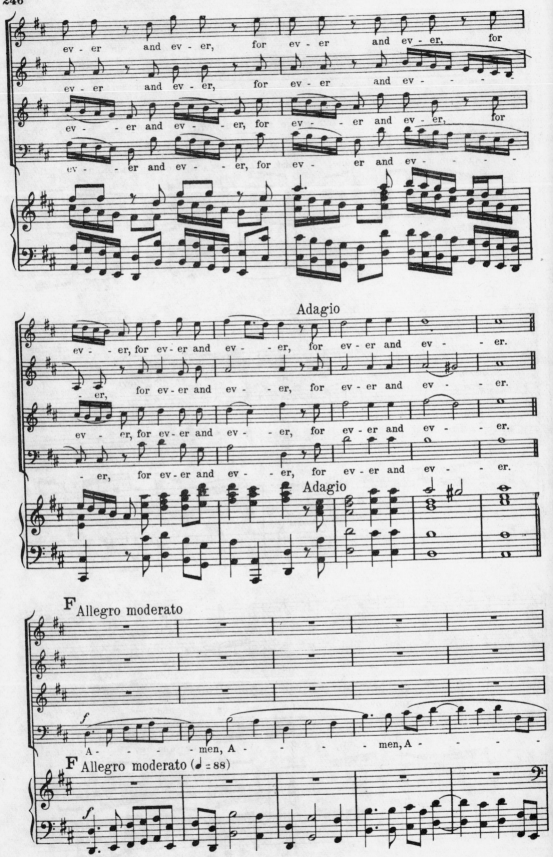

22945